PET LAUGHS

Copyright © 2021 by

NEVADA THORNTON

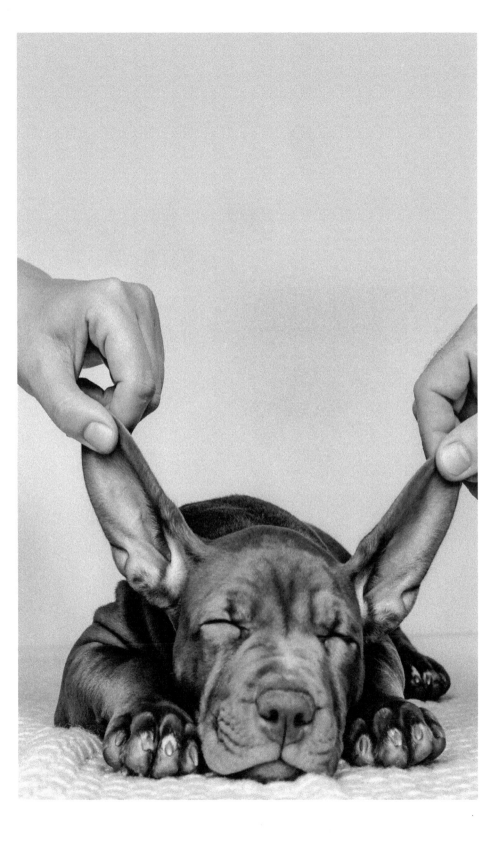

More titles in this series:

Beautiful Flowers
Adorable Babies
Pet Laughs
Cooking And Recipes
Farm Life
Beautiful Butterflies
Beautiful Birds
Beach Holiday

Adorable Babies

NEVADA THORNTON

Beautiful Flowers

NEVADA THORNTON

Food and Cooking

NEVADA THORNTON

CPSIA information can be obtained
at www.ICGtesting.com
Printed in the USA
LVHW072150310821
696637LV00028B/1092